C000271911

Merry Christmas

with Creature Comforts

First published 2004 by Pan Macmillan Ltd
Pan Macmillan, 20 New Wharf Road, London N1 9RR
Basingstoke and Oxford
Associated companies throughout the world
www.panmacmillan.com

ISBN 07522 1578 7

Produced under license by Aardman Animations © and ™ Aardman Ltd 2004

Text © Pan Macmillan Ltd 2004

2 4 6 8 9 7 5 3 1

A CIP catalogue record for this book is available from the British Library.

Design by Dan Newman @ Perfect Bound Ltd
Layout and text by seagulls

Printed by Proost, Belgium

Aardman presents

Merry Christmas

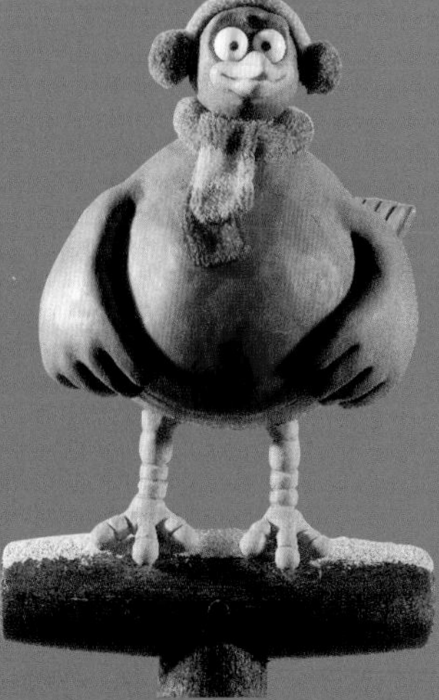

with Creature Comforts

'I like just sitting down, eating, drinking and being merry.'

fluffy

'I never seem to get the presents I really want, just rubbish things. That's if I get anything at all.'

'I go everywhere at Christmas time with my mistletoe attached to my glasses and then I can kiss all the chaps that I come into contact with.'

charlie

'Jingle bells,
Batman smells,
Robin's flown away.'

'I still get a bit of a thrill out of it after all these years. Brings me back to my childhood.'

gary & nigel

'Christmas is something to do with God.'

'I think that even
if you hate turkey,
you've got to have
it at Christmas.
I think it's the law.'

trixie &
captain cuddlepuss

'I like seeing friends and just sort of taking it easy. And just being comfortable but not extravagant.'

'I'm always starving.'

'It's just salad and spuds for me, I'm afraid.'

trousers

'I think it should go back to what it was like... the old pagan days.'

'Being appreciated, that's the nicest part of it.'

'There's always an argument, isn't there? And sometimes even the turkey ends up on the wall.'

'Christmas is
a time when
people go out
and just go mad.'

gary & nigel

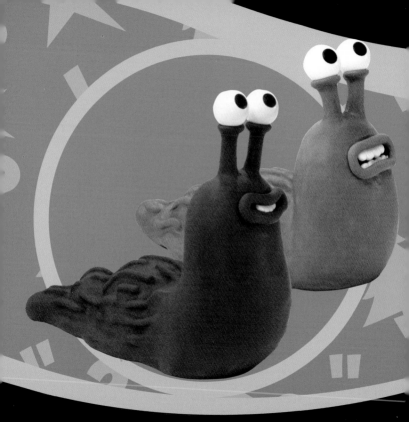

turkey

'I do feel that I'm being pulled in all directions. They are all going to get a piece of me.'

'Turkey butties with a bit of stuffing on it. You can't beat it.'

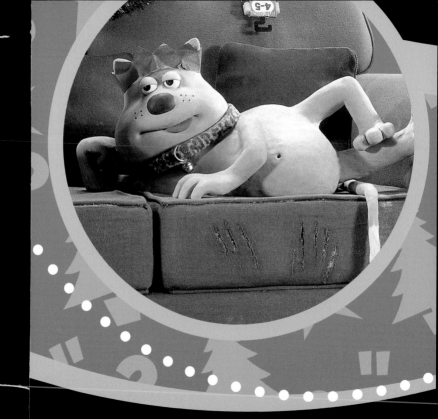

'What can a cat do with a Christmas card?'

'I think people get more stupid with their money at Christmas.'

spanner & trousers

christmas tree

'I love dressing up at Christmas. The flashing earrings and all the tacky stuff.'

"When I close my eyes I go "One reindeer, two reindeer, three reindeer." I count them and that's what makes me go to sleep.'

fluffy

'It's best
if you're
a kid.'

'If you think it's tough for us, imagine what it's like for Santa.'

callum & giles